Performing Parables

by

Christine Holmes

MOORLEY'S Print & Publishing

MOORLEY'S Print & Publishing
23 Park Rd., Ilkeston, Derbys DE7 5DA
Tel/Fax: (0115) 932 0643
ISBN 0 81071 470 5

CONTENTS

Page

HE NEVER DID!

Luke 15:11-32

Cast:

Older brother
Friend

SCENE: *Older brother's bedroom.*

Friend: He never did!

Older brother: He did, I tell you. He lost the lot!

Friend: Lost the lot!

Older brother: Yes, he lost the lot!

Friend: Not your half as well?

Older brother: No, not my half as well. Just his half. But now that there's only my half left, my dad says we've got to share that as well. That means I'm only going to get a quarter, and he'll have had three quarters.

Friend: Not fair, is it?

Older brother: No, it's not.

Friend: And what did your dad say when he came back. I bet he didn't half catch it?

Older brother: Catch it? All he caught was a new set of clothes and a fatted calf.

Friend: Fatted calf?

Older brother: Yes, my fatted calf as well. I'd been fattening that calf up for the next bar-BQ. And now it's gone.

5

Friend:	Not fair, is it.
Older brother:	No, it's not.
Friend:	And your dad. Didn't he even tell him off?
Older brother:	No he did not.
Friend:	Mine would have done if it had been me. He'd have half killed me for doing that!
Older brother:	Yes, knowing your dad, I expect he would.
Friend:	Yea. And you mean to say he didn't even ask him where the money'd gone?
Older brother:	Nope. No questions asked.
Friend:	Well, I don't know.
Older brother:	No, I don't know either.
Friend:	Then what happened, after he came back and got some new gear?
Older brother:	We're having a big party with the fatted calf.
Friend:	Are you going?
Older brother:	Am I going? What do you think?
Friend:	No, I wouldn't go, either.
Older brother:	I said to my dad, I've worked here all the time he's been gone and you never had a party for me. Now look what he's done. Been and gone and gone off with half your money, lost the lot, come crawling back and you give him a party! And with my fatted calf as well!
Friend:	And what did your dad say?

Older brother:	What did my dad say! He said that I didn't need a party as I was always with him.
Friend:	Huh. That's not a very good reason.
Older brother:	No, I didn't think so either.
Friend:	Then what did he say?
Older brother:	He said that my brother had been lost and now he was found and that's why we should celebrate.
Friend:	Ooh, my dad wouldn't have said that.
Older brother:	No, you're right, he wouldn't. What do you think your dad would have done?
Friend:	Well, for starters, he wouldn't have let me have half his money. Then if I'd gone and lost the lot he wouldn't have had me back in the house, never mind buy me some new gear and then have a party for me. No fear. If I'd done what your kid had done, I'd have been a gonner by now. I'd have known it would have been no use coming back. Do you think your dad would have done the same if it was you who'd gone off with the money?
Older brother:	Yes, I think he would, at that.
Friend:	And what would your kid have thought if it had been you who'd done it?
Older brother:	Hmm. Probably the same as me. He'd have been as mad as ......
Friend:	Yes, I think you're right. Knowing your kid, he would have been even madder than you are.
Older brother:	Yes, you're right. He would have.
Friend:	I sometimes wish my dad was more like your dad.

Older brother: Whatever for?

Friend: Well, look what he's just done for your kid. And you say
                   he would have done just the same for you. My dad
                   wouldn't have done it for anybody. It wouldn't have
                   mattered if it had been our kid or me. We'd have both
                   been for the chop. Yes, I wish my dad was a bit more like
                   your dad.

Older brother: Yes, I suppose you're right.

Friend: What's that smell?

Older brother: Smell? Oh that. It's the fatted calf. It should just be
                   about roasted by now.

Friend: It smells good, doesn't it. I aren't half hungry. I haven't
                   eaten since dinner time, have you?

Older brother: I haven't eaten all day, I was so mad.

Friend: Do you think it would be alright if I went to the party
                   with you?

Older brother: I'm not going to his party.

Friend: Oh, go on. You've said yourself that your dad would have
                   done the same for you and that your kid would have felt
                   just the same way as you're feeling. Forget it. Forgive
                   him. Come on, you know you love fatted calf sandwiches.
                   Come on.

Older brother: Oh, all right. I suppose I'd better go.

Friend: Fatted calf in a bread bun, here we come. Beats a Big
                   Mac any day!

*If space allows the prodigal son and father could also mime their parts as
the older brother and his friend are talking about them.*

THE END

8

I WILL CALL YOU BY YOUR NAME

Matthew 18:12-13

Luke 15:1-7

Cast:

Shepherd

Shepherd's Friend

SCENE: *In the wilderness*

Shepherd's friend: What did you say its name was?

Shepherd: Lucky.

Shepherd's friend: Lucky! Not so lucky tonight, is it? Getting itself lost like this.

Shepherd: No he's not, is he? I wonder how far he's strayed tonight.

Shepherd's friend: You mean it's not unusual for it to go wandering off like this?

Shepherd: Oh no. He's missing most nights, only I can usually find him on my own.

Shepherd's friend: If I had a sheep that went missing most nights, and I had to leave all my other sheep and go looking for it, I'm afraid my sheep would have to stay missing.

Shepherd: Oh I couldn't do that. I couldn't leave him out in the wilderness all alone. *(Starts to shout)* Lucky, Lucky, where are you? Lucky.

Shepherd's friend: Lucky. Lucky.

Shepherd: Lucky, Lucky, come on now.

Shepherd's friend:	How many sheep did you say you had?
Shepherd:	One hundred.
Shepherd's friend:	And where are the other ninety nine?
Shepherd:	I've had to leave them behind.
Shepherd's friend:	All alone in the wilderness?
Shepherd:	Yes, but I'm sure they'll be all right.
Shepherd's friend:	If you've got one hundred sheep, and they all look alike, how do you know which one's missing?
Shepherd:	Oh, that's easy. I know all their names. They're all my friends.
Shepherd's friend:	Friends. Sheep? They all look alike to me.
Shepherd:	No they're not. Every one is different. We spend so much time together that I give every one of them a special name. *(Starts to shout again).* Lucky. Lucky.
Shepherd's friend:	If you've still got ninety nine sheep left, why are you bothering with just one that's gone missing? I'd just leave him if I were you.
Shepherd:	I can't do that. Every one of my sheep is just as precious as the others. I've got to go and find him.
Shepherd's friend:	Lucky. Lucky, come on you pest.
Shepherd:	He won't come for you, you know. My sheep only know my voice and they'll only come when I call.
Shepherd's friend:	Your sheep only know your voice? It's a well known fact that all sheep are stupid. How can a stupid sheep recognise your voice? Lucky, Lucky.

Shepherd:	I tell you, they do know my voice. Just as I know all their names. I bet I could go on that T.V. programme, what's it called, "You Bet", and name every single one of my sheep, even though they all look alike to everybody else.
Shepherd's friend:	Ahh, rubbish. A sheep's a sheep. Only good for one thing, no, sorry, two. A nice sheepskin jacket and a good lamb stew.
Shepherd:	Not my sheep! You can have a jacket from my sheep but they'll never end up in anybody's stew!
Shepherd's friend:	Then why do you bother with them then?
Shepherd:	Because they're all my friends.
Shepherd's friend:	I'll bet you wish you had better friends than that when you're out in the wilderness at night with the lions and bears roaming round, don't you?
Shepherd:	No I don't. My sheep are company enough. And they know that I'm there to go in front of them and protect them from any lions and bears that are around.
Shepherd's friend:	Have you killed any?
Shepherd:	Any what?
Shepherd's friend:	Lions and bears.
Shepherd:	Just one bear, so far.
Shepherd's friend:	Wow. I bet that was something to see. *(Starts to shout again)* Lucky, Lucky.
Shepherd:	I told you he won't come for you. He'll only come for me. Lucky, Lucky.
Shepherd's friend:	What's that noise?

Shepherd:	What noise?
Shepherd's friend:	I thought I heard a noise coming from over there in that bush.
Shepherd:	Shhhh. Listen. Lucky, Lucky is that you?
Sheep:	Baa, baaaa.
Shepherd:	Oh, Lucky, oh thank goodness I've found you. Help me get him out of this bush. He's caught by his long coat.
Shepherd's friend:	Looks like Lucky could do with a hair cut.
Shepherd:	You're right there. Help me pull him out. That's right. Now help me to get him on my shoulders.
Shepherd's friend:	On your shoulders?
Shepherd:	Yes, so that I can carry him home.
Shepherd's friend:	Carry him home? He's got four legs, you've only got two. Let him walk.
Shepherd:	Oh, no. I'm so glad to have found my lost sheep that I'll carry him home rejoicing.
Shepherd's friend:	When we get back and he has his hair cut, do you think I could have it for a new jacket, for helping you to find him?

THE END

TABLES TURNED

Luke 14:7-14

Cast:

Michelle	Charlotte's mum
Michelle's mum	Katie
Charlotte	

SCENE 1: *Michelle's house*

SCENE 2: *Charlotte's house*

SCENE 3: *Katie's house*

SCENE 1

Michelle: Mum, I saw a really great outfit in Top Man yesterday. Can I have it to go to Katie's party in? It was only £49.99?

Michelle's mum: Only £49.99! That tee-shirt you got last week was only £15.99. When I was a girl if we paid £5.00 for a tee-shirt it was ridiculous. £15.99 for a scrap of a thing like that. What your dad's going to say when he sees you in it I don't know. I don't like you going around outside with all your midriff bare. I just doesn't seem decent to me.

Michelle: Oh. mum, everybody does nowadays. Don't be so old fashioned. Can I have that new outfit for Katie's party? Go on, mum. Say yes. I don't want everybody to think I can't afford new clothes. Anyway, if I go in that outfit Katie might let me stay the night.

Michelle's mum: What's a new outfit got to do with you staying all night?

Michelle: Well, I know Katie's seen this outfit as well, and her mum says she can't have it, so if she lets me stay the night, then I'll let her borrow it for the next party.

13

	Nobody's ever stayed at Katie's house all night. All the other girls'll be so mad if I get to stay at Katie's house all night. I'll feel so important and everybody else will be so jealous. Go on, mum. Can I have it?
Michelle's mum:	Well, I suppose so. If it means you get to stay at Katie's house all night, then it could be worth it. I must say, I've never even been invited to Katie's house, even for a cup of coffee. Her mum thinks she's a cut above the rest of us. If you get to spend the night there, I'll come round for you the morning after and she'll surely ask me in for a cup of coffee or something. It could be a way in for me too.
Michelle:	Yes, mum, that's the way to look at it. You get me the new outfit, and I'll get you into Katie's house. Then we'll have something to tell the rest of them about. Come on, let's go to town now.

SCENE 2

Charlotte:	Mum, I've been invited to Katie's party but I don't want to go.
Charlotte's mum:	You don't want to go? Why ever not? You've been wanting to go to Katie's house for ages.
Charlotte:	I know, but I've changed my mind.
Charlotte's mum:	Whatever for?
Charlotte:	Because I don't.
Charlotte's mum:	Now come on, what's the matter?
Charlotte:	I just don't want to go, that's all.
Charlotte's mum:	You can't just change your mind like that. You only said yesterday that you wanted to go.

14

Charlotte:	I know, but that was yesterday, wasn't it? Besides ....
Charlotte's mum:	Besides what? What's happened since yesterday? You only saw Michelle yesterday.
Charlotte:	I know I did. That's just the problem!
Charlotte's mum:	What's the problem?
Charlotte:	She is. That Michelle.
Charlotte's mum:	Michelle? I thought she was one of your best friends.
Charlotte:	So did I.
Charlotte's mum:	Well, what's happened then?
Charlotte:	Nothing.
Charlotte's mum:	Come on, something's happened. You can't just fall out with somebody for nothing.
Charlotte:	It wasn't for nothing.
Charlotte's mum:	I can see that, so if it wasn't for nothing, then it must have been for something.
Charlotte:	It doesn't matter.
Charlotte's mum:	Yes, it does matter. Won't you tell me what it's about? Go on, tell me.
Charlotte:	It was nothing. It was only about a new outfit she's got.
Charlotte's mum:	A new outfit. What's that got to do with Katie's party? Oh I see.. Michelle's got a new outfit, has she?
Charlotte:	Yes she has, and I know I can't have one, so I'm not going to the party.

Charlotte's mum:	You can still go to the party. You've got lots of nice things to wear.
Charlotte:	I know, but Michelle says that she thinks that Katie will ask her to stay over all night because of this new outfit.
Charlotte's mum:	What's so special about this new outfit?
Charlotte:	Well, it's one that Katie saw in Top Man, but her mum wouldn't let her have it, and now Michelle's mum has bought her it to go to the party in and Michelle thinks that Katie will let her stay the night so that she can borrow her new outfit .
Charlotte's mum:	Well, I don't think that's a very good basis for a friendship. That shouldn't stop you going to the party. Did you want to stay all night as well?
Charlotte:	No, I didn't. Well, I wouldn't have minded if Katie had asked me, but Katie never asks anybody to stay overnight, so I've never thought much about it. It would be nice to be asked, though.
Charlotte's mum:	Well, if you're not bothered whether you're asked to stay all night or not, why can't you just go to the party? You know that we can't afford another new outfit, but you look nice in anything you wear. I must say, if your dad saw you in some of the things that Michelle wears he wouldn't let you out of the house, never mind stay out all night. Go on, never mind Michelle. You just go and enjoy yourself.

SCENE 3

Katie:	Hi, Charlotte. Nice to see you. Do you want some food or some Appletize? It's over there. Can you help yourself. I'll be with you in a minute. I just have to make sure that everyone's OK. Don't disappear will you, I've got something I want to ask you.

Enter MICHELLE

Michelle: Hi, Katie. *(Spins round to show off her new outfit)* How do you like it then?

Katie: Like what? Oh, you mean the outfit. It looks OK I suppose, but I'm glad I didn't get it now. I saw two other girls wearing it when I went to the concert last night.

Michelle: What? But I thought you said you wanted it as well?

Katie: Well, I did last week when we saw it in Top Man, but I knew my mum wouldn't let me go about wearing something like that, and when I saw those other two girls in it last night, I'm glad I didn't get it. Anyway, it's nice to see you. The food's over there. What have you got in your bag? It looks like you've come to stay the weekend with a bag that size.

MICHELLE stomps over to CHARLOTTE

Charlotte: Hi there, Michelle. Oh you do look nice. Your mum let you have it after all then?

Michelle: What? Oh this, what does it matter, anyway?

Charlotte: What do you mean? Hasn't Katie asked you to stay the night? I see you've got your bag.

Michelle: No she hasn't. I didn't want to stay, anyway.

KATIE joins up with them.

Katie: Hi there, you two. How do you think the party's going? I've never had a party here before, so I wasn't sure if anyone would want to come. I'm so glad you both could come. Charlotte, do you think if you rang your mum she'd let you stay the night?

Charlotte: Me? Stay the night?

17

Katie:	Yes. Don't you want to?
Charlotte:	Yes, I'd love to, but I thought ..... *(looking at MICHELLE)*
Katie:	That's all right then. I'll show you where the phone is and then you can ring your mum. Don't worry about clothes and things. You can borrow some of mine. And when your mum comes for you in the morning, she can always come in for a cup of coffee with my mum and a chat. It's time my mum got to know some of my friends' mums. *(KATIE and CHARLOTTE walk off together)*.

MICHELLE is left alone, fuming.

Could read the passage from Luke's gospel now. The first shall be last and the last shall be first.

THE END

ANY OLD RAGS?

Matthew 9:16-17
Mark 2:21-22
Luke 5:36-39

Cast:

Vicky	Fred
Vicky's mum	Joe
Hayley	

SCENE 1: *Vicky's house*
SCENE 2: *At the disco*
SCENE 3: *Fred's patio*

SCENE 1:

Vicky: Mum, will you sew a patch on these jeans, please?

Mum: Sew a patch on them? I thought you only bought them yesterday.

Vicky: I did.

Mum: So why do you want a patch on them? How have you managed to get a hole in them already?

Vicky: With scissors, of course.

Mum: What! Which scissors?

Vicky: Those scissors you keep in your sewing cupboard.

Mum: But how did you manage to cut a hole in your new jeans? Why were you messing about with my scissors?

Vicky: I wasn't messing about, mum, I cut a hole in them on purpose.

Mum: You cut a hole in them on purpose?

Vicky: Yes.

Mum:	Whatever for? Are you wrong in your head?
Vicky:	No. I just wanted my jeans to be patched, like everyone else's.
Mum:	Patched! How much did you pay for them?
Vicky:	£49.99.
Mum:	£49.99 and now you want a patch on them? Why didn't you say you wanted patched jeans? I wouldn't have thrown your others away if I'd known. You could have had those old ones patched up.
Vicky:	No, no. It wouldn't be the same. You don't wear old jeans with patches on, only new ones.
Mum:	Well it certainly wasn't like that when I was young.
Vicky:	No, mum, it never was, was it?
Mum:	You just watch it, my girl. Let me look. *(Grabs jeans from VICKY)* You really have made a mess of these, now haven't you?
Vicky:	Aw, mum. Just get your sewing machine out and sew a patch on, will you?
Mum:	And where am I supposed to get some material to match?
Vicky:	Oh, it doesn't have to match. If it matched it wouldn't be the same.
Mum:	If it matched it jolly well would be the same, my girl.
Vicky:	No, I mean, it wouldn't be right if it matched. It's not the fashion to have matching patches. They've got to be different. Anything will do.
Mum:	Anything will not do. If I'm going to spend my time mending your new jeans then anything certainly will not do. Give them here.
Vicky:	Mum, let me choose my own patch, will you?

Both exit.

SCENE: 2

Vicky: Hey, you lot, how do you like my new jeans?

Hayley: Hey, I like your patchwork, Vicky. How did you manage to persuade your mum to let you cut your new jeans up?

Vicky: I didn't. I just cut them up and then she had to find some old stuff to patch them with. Great, isn't it?

Hayley: Yeah. Great. Are you ready to do this next dance? You have to be fit to dance like this especially in those jeans. I've never seen any as tight as that before. *(Both girls start to dance energetically).*

Vicky: No, they are a nice tight fit, aren't they?

Hayley: Yea. Do you think your mum would sew some patches on mine?

Vicky: Yes, I'm sure she would. They feel great. Ooops!

Hayley: What's the matter?

Vicky: My patch. I think it's coming off. Oh, have a look, will you?

Hayley: Yes, you're right, it's hanging off. Oh heck, what are you going to do? I can see everything you've got on underneath.

Vicky: Oh, no. It must be that old material my mum used. She said it wouldn't do to sew old material onto new, but I thought it would look great. Now what am I going to do?

Hayley: I think we'd better go home and ask your mum to find some suitable material and start all over again. Don't you?

Vicky: Knowing my mum, she won't. They'll be straight into the rag bag.

SCENE: 3

Fred: Now then, Joe, how about trying some of my new home-brew? I just made it yesterday.

Joe: Great. I remember your last lot. Phew. Powerful stuff that was. How I got home from your house that night I do not remember.

Fred: Well, it's the same recipe this time. Here, have a glass.

Joe: *(Having a drink)* Great stuff that. How did you manage to find enough new bottles to put it in when it was ready for bottling?

Fred: Oh, I didn't bother about that. I'd got loads of old bottles left over from last time. You drank enough to keep me in bottles for six months. Don't tell me you don't remember.

Joe: Oh, yes I do!

Fred: Well then. What's the point in buying new bottles when there were all those in my garage waiting to be used again?

Joe: I thought I'd read somewhere that you should never put new beer into old bottles.

Fred: Old wives tale! Load of rubbish.

Joe: Have you ever done it before?

Fred: No. But if you listened to all these old wives tales that are going around you'd never do anything.

Joe: No, I suppose you're right. Can I have another, please?

Fred: 'Course you can. That's what it's there for. Help yourself. There's plenty more where that came from.

Joe: Did you hear what happened to our Vicky's new jeans?

Fred: No, what happened?

Joe: Can I have another drink.

Fred: Go ahead, help yourself. *(Passes bottle to JOE who pours one out for FRED).* Ta, thanks. Don't mind if I do.

Joe: Well, the daft kid bought these new jeans. Paid the earth for them, she did, then she cut a hole in them, in the back and expected her mother to sew a patch on.

Fred: Whatever did she do a daft thing like that for?

Joe: Fashion. You know what kids are nowadays. Anything goes as long as it's in fashion.

Fred: Then what happened?

Joe: Well, she went to this disco. Started dancing in these tight jeans, and the patch flew off, showing all she's got!

Fred: The daft beggar. Has she never heard of the saying that you can't patch a new garment with old cloth?

Joe: Mustn't have. Can I have another one, please?

Fred: Help yourself. Can't go wrong if you listen to these old sayings, can you? There's no smoke without fire is what I always say.

Joe: Fred, what's that funny noise coming from your garage?

Fred: What funny noise?

Joe: It sounds like glass breaking.

Fred: Glass breaking?

Joe: Yes. And something's running out from under the door. It looks a bit brown and sticky to me. What have you got in your garage that's made of glass with brown, sticky stuff in it?

Fred: Nothing that I know of. Only my home brew. Oh no ....

THE END

JUDGING OTHERS

Matthew 7 : 1 - 5 and 15 : 14 - 20
Luke 6 : 36 - 42

Cast:

Jesus	Friend
Father	Policeman
Son *(dressed like a*	Student
Mohican / punk rocker etc.)	Two Hikers.

SCENE: *Outdoors*

JESUS is standing in the background to each act listening to the conversations.

ACT 1

Mohican / punk rocker etc (young person) walks by with head averted so his father does not recognise him.

Father: *(Talking to audience)*
Did you see him? I don't know what the world's coming to. I don't know what today's parents are thinking about letting their kids go around dressed like that. And the hairstyles! Don't they teach barbers how to cut hair nowadays? Mind you, it's all Unisex hairdressing today, isn't it? You can't get a decent short back and sides any more. And the clothes they all wear! I wouldn't be seen dead dressed like that, and neither would any of my family. That lot, they're all up to no good, you know - mugging old ladies, robbing banks, going joy-riding. It's all the teachers' fault. A few whacks with a cane never did me any harm, did it?

Young person walks by again, this time facing the speaker.

Young person: Hi, dad.

Jesus: Don't judge others and then you won't be judged, for others will treat you as you treat them.

Both exit, leaving JESUS still listening.

ACT 2

Friend: Do you know what my friend did the other day? He ran over a hedgehog with his car. I've told him not to drive too fast on those narrow, country roads round where he lives, but has he ever listened to me? No, he has not. I said to him, "One day you're going to hit something, that's for sure. Twenty miles an hour is quite fast enough for the sort of road you live on". But what can you expect from the young nowadays? They don't want to listen to the likes of us. *(Enter POLICEMAN, giving paper to speaker).* Ooh, it's a letter for me. I bet it's about my neighbour, doing something else wrong in his car. Oh, it's not! It's a summons! What for? For dangerous driving? Seventy-five miles an hour in a restricted area? When was that? First of January, 1.15 a.m. I don't remember .... Oh, first of January, New Year's Day - after that party. I don't even remember driving home, never mind going at seventy-five miles an hour. What else does it say? I ran over a pedestrian. I don't remember ..... *(Walks off, head in hands).*

Jesus: Why do you bother about the speck in someone else's eye - his little fault - when a plank (a big fault) is in your own? Hypocrite! Get rid of your own plank and then you might be able to see well enough to deal with his little speck.

ACT 3

Two hikers enter from opposite sides, both with different maps.

1st Hiker: *(Looking at a map)*
I can't understand this map. I just can't find where I am on it and it's getting dark.

2nd Hiker: *(Looking at map)*
I don't understand this map. I just can't find where I am on it and it's getting dark.

1st Hiker: Oh, here comes somebody who looks like they know where they're going. I'll ask him.

2nd Hiker:	Oh, here comes somebody who looks like they know where they're going. I'll ask him.
1st Hiker:	Excuse me, but I think I'm a bit lost. Can you show me on my map where I am, please?
2nd Hiker:	Sure, show me your map. I can't understand my map but I might be able to understand yours, and then I'll know where we both are, won't I?
1st Hiker:	Er, yes, I suppose so.
2nd Hiker:	Now then, let me see. Ah, yes, I thought so. You've got the wrong map. No wonder you can't find where you are on it. Here, look at my map, and then you'll know where you are on it.
1st Hiker:	*(Putting away his own map)* Oh, thanks a lot. Let's have a look. Do you think that big gully shown on this map is anywhere near here?
2nd Hiker:	No, I don't think we're anywhere near that at all. I think we're here, right in the middle of this flat bit of land. It's getting dark so I think we should set off over this flat bit of land straight away and try and make for this main road that's shown here, and then maybe we can thumb a lift back to town before it gets really dark.
1st Hiker:	All right then. Let's go while we can still see where we're going.

(Both exit the same way - then a terrific crash sounds off stage as they both scream out that they are falling down the gully).

Jesus:	What good is it for one blind man to lead another? He will fall into a ditch and pull the other down with him.

ACT 4

Student:	Do you know, I don't know why I bother going to school/college? My teachers/lecturers don't know anything. They don't know what they're talking about. They just can't

keep up with this day and age. Their heads are still in the clouds about their own times at college. Not that they could ever have learnt much there. All they ever do is keep on telling us we must go to school every day, sit down and listen, study for stupid exams and threaten us with the worst if we don't. Well what does it matter anyway? Who's bothered whether we go to school or not? Exams are just a doddle. There's nothing to it. I'm just off to look at the results to see how well I've done. *(Walks towards a notice board)*. I know my future depends on these results, but I'll have done all right. And it'll be all my own work, because my teachers were rubbish. Now, where's my name? Oh flipping heck, it's in alphabetical order. I never could remember all the alphabet. Oh, here I am. What does a "U" stand for at the side of every subject? I thought there would be an "A" or at least a "B". What does "U" stand for? Oh, here, it tells you at the bottom. "U" stands for unclassified? What does that mean? It doesn't mean that I haven't .... Does it? Oh what am I going to do? What am I going tell my dad? *(Runs off)*.

Jesus: How can a student know more than his teacher? But if he works hard he may learn as much.

(All come back on stage to listen to JESUS)

Jesus: Evil words come from an evil heart and spoil the one who says them. A good man produces good deeds from a good heart. Whatever is in the heart overflows into speech so try to show as much compassion as your Father does, and never criticise or condemn or it will come back on you. Go easy on others and they will do the same for you.

THE END

SOWING SEEDS

Matthew 13 : 3 - 23
Mark 4 : 1 - 20
Luke 8 : 4 - 15

Cast:

Jesus	Birds
Disciples	Rocky ground
Farmer	Hot sun
People being paths	Thorns
	Good soil

SCENE: *A field*

Props - placards to be held up to show who is what or costumes to show same, big seeds.

Jesus: *(as commentator)*
A farmer was sowing grain in his fields. As he scattered the seed across the ground some fell beside a path and the birds came and ate it.

FARMER scatters his seed (big seeds) on the paths, who hold their hands over their ears and turn away, whilst the birds come and take the seeds away.

Jesus: A farmer was sowing grain in his fields. As he scattered the seed across the ground some fell on rocky soil where there wasn't much earth; the plants grew up quickly enough in the shallow soil, but the hot sun soon scorched them and they withered and died, for they hadn't rooted.

FARMER scatters his seeds on rocky soil which quickly shoot up and stretch out towards the hot sun, and just as quickly fall down dead.

Jesus: A farmer was sowing grain in his fields. As he scattered the seed across the ground some fell among thorns and the thorns choked them.

FARMER scatters his seeds among the thorns who immediately grab the seeds and rip them to pieces.

Jesus: A farmer was sowing grain in his fields. As he scattered the seed across the ground some fell on good soil and produced a crop that was 30, 60 and even 100 times as much as he had planted.

FARMER scatters his seeds on the good ground who grow up, and stand up and listen to JESUS, and show placards with numbers 30, 60 and 100 written on them.

Disciples: Now that's very interesting, Jesus, or it would be if we knew what you were talking about. Why do you always tell stories in parables? Why can't you explain it to us simply?

Jesus: OK, here's what it means. The hard path means the hard hearts of the people who don't want to listen to the Good News and don't understand it. Satan then comes along and snatches the Good News away.

PATH and BIRDS, meanwhile, re-enact what they did when the FARMER was scattering the seeds.

Jesus: The shallow, rocky soil means the hearts of the people who hear about the Good News and receive it with joy, but they don't have much depth to their lives and so the seeds don't root very deeply, and after a while, when trouble or persecution comes along, their enthusiasm fails and they drop out.

Rocky ground and hot sun, meanwhile, re-enact what they did when the FARMER was scattering the seeds.

Jesus: The ground covered with thorns means those who hear the Good News, but worrying about things and wanting more money and things choke out God's word and they do less and less for God.

The thorns, meanwhile, re-enact what they did when the FARMER was scattering the seeds.

Jesus: The good ground means the hearts of those who listen to the Good News and understand it and go out and bring 30, 60 and even 100 more people into the Kingdom.

The good ground, meanwhile, re-enact what they did when the FARMER was scattering the seeds.

Disciples: Thanks, Jesus, now we know what you mean. But what about this Kingdom of Heaven, what's it like and who's going there?

Jesus: I'll tell you a story about what the Kingdom of Heaven is like. It's like another farmer who sowed good seed in his field. One night, when he was asleep, his enemy came and sowed thistles among his seeds and when the seeds began to grow the thistles began to grow as well. The farmer's men came and asked if they ought to pull out all the thistles, but the farmer said not to as they might pull up the seeds as well. He told them to let them all grow together until harvest time and then the reapers would sort out the thistles and burn them and the wheat would be put into the barn.

Disciples: Now we think we see what you mean. Do you mean we can all grow up together and do everything together, good people and bad, but when God wants to, He'll do the sorting out, not us, and He'll be the one who decides who gets into the Kingdom of Heaven and who doesn't? Is that what you mean?

Jesus: Yes it is.

THE END

THE CASE OF THE MISSING JEWELLERY

Luke 15 : 8 - 10

Cast:

Stephanie

Becky

Jesus

SCENE: *Becky's house*

Becky: Do you know, Stephanie, at last I've managed to save up enough money to buy my tenth gold earring?

Stephanie: That's great. Now you can wear five in each ear.

Becky: I know, Stephanie. I'm really excited about it. It's taken me ever so long to manage to save up enough to buy ten gold earrings. Ever since I lost that job in the supermarket and that's nearly three months since.

Stephanie: I know, Becky. It really is hard to manage when you've been out of a job for so long. I think you've done really well to be able to get ten gold earrings, even in three months. Some girls who haven't a job would have given up trying ages since.

Becky: I know, Stephanie, I really am lucky. My mum and dad have been very good even though they're not well off themselves. They've managed to give me a bit of spending money now and again.

Stephanie: I know, Becky. Anyway, now you've got your tenth gold earring you really have something to celebrate.

Becky: Yes, I know. I could never go out with only four rings in each ear. It just didn't look right, somehow, but now I can go out and feel proud of myself for once.

Stephanie: You can that, Becky. Look, do you want me to go with you to get your ears pierced? Then I can tell you how they look?

Becky: Oh, would you do that for me, Steph? That'll be great. Just you wait here while I go upstairs and fetch them down.

(BECKY leaves the stage. A scream is heard from off stage)

Stephanie: Becky, what's the matter? Have you fallen? Have you hurt yourself?

(BECKY comes back on stage, shaking)

Stephanie: Whatever's the matter, Becky? You look as if you've seen a ghost.

Becky: Oh, Stephanie, I must be going mad. Will you count these gold earrings for me, please? I've just counted them twice, and there only seems to be nine, not ten. Will you count them, please, and tell me I've made a mistake. *(Hands the earrings to STEPHANIE).*

Stephanie: *(counting the earrings)*
One, two, three, four, five, six, seven ...... Oh, just a minute, I'd better start again. One, two, three, four, five, six, seven ...... eight .... Oh, Becky, you've not made a mistake, there are only nine.

Becky: Only nine? But I had ten, I know I had ten.

Stephanie: Are you sure there were ten, Becky? Are you sure that your new one is your tenth and not your ninth?

Becky: Of course I'm sure. Haven't I been saving up for them long enough? The number of times I've counted them, waiting for the time to come when I could afford to get the tenth one, then I could get my ears pierced properly.

Stephanie: Well all I can say, Becky, is that you must have lost one. Are you sure you didn't drop one when you went to fetch them to show me just now?

Becky: No I didn't. I would have heard it drop and roll away if I had done, wouldn't I?

34

Stephanie:	Yes I suppose you would. Can you remember where you were the last time you had them out?
Becky:	Oh I don't know. Let me think. Where was I? I know, I was right here in this room. I remember, because it was when I was counting up my money to see if I had enough to get the last one. I remember counting the earrings and then wrapping them all up and putting them away again.
Stephanie:	Well you must have dropped one then and not heard it fall. Let's have a look around, shall we? It's probably rolled away into a corner.
Becky:	Have you time to stay and help me, Stephanie? It's getting a bit dark. I'd better put the light on so we can see what we're doing.
Stephanie:	That's better, Becky. I'll stay with you until you find it. I've no need to rush home just yet. Come on, let's get searching. Help me to pull this bench away from the wall.
Becky:	I think I'd better take up all the rugs and give them a shake and then throw them outside. Then I'll get the Hoover out and sweep the whole room. You watch for the earring shining, or listen to see if it goes up the Hoover will you?
Stephanie:	Right-ho. I'll help you with the rugs, and then watch while you Hoover.

(They both shake the rugs, throw them outside, and BECKY Hoovers the floor.)

Becky:	*(Hoovering vigorously)* Can you see anything yet, Stephanie?
Stephanie:	No, not yet, Becky. How about trying over there, in that corner? Push the Hoover under the table there.
Becky:	OK. How about that? Did anything roll out then?
Stephanie:	No, not yet. How about trying over there, under the drawers?

Becky: All right. At least mum's house is getting a good clean. She'll wonder what on earth's come over me, doing the Hoovering for her. At least she'll be glad for me when we find it.

Stephanie: That's the right way to look at it, Becky. You said, "when we find it", not "if we find it". We'll find it all right. Try over in that last corner. I'm sure it'll be there.

Becky: Any luck this time? Oh, what was that? I'm sure I heard something then.

Stephanie: *(coughing)*
You're making so much dust, Becky, that I can't see a thing. Just stop a minute and I'll see if I can see anything.

Becky: Look over there! There it is! Eureka - I've found it. *(Starts to dance around with the broom)*.

Stephanie: Is this a private dance or can anybody join in?

Becky: Don't be so daft. Come on with me to get my ears pierced and then we can go down town and celebrate with everybody because I've found my earring.

Stephanie: Don't you think we ought to put the rugs back and move the Hoover away first, before your mum gets back?

(Enter JESUS)

Jesus: I tell you, there is rejoicing before the angels in heaven over one lost sinner who repents.

THE END

THE PARABLE OF THE VINEYARD

Matthew 21 : 33 - 46
Mark 12 :1 - 12
Luke 20 : 9 - 19

Cast:

Vineyard owner	Three servants
Builders	Man's Son
Tenants	Jesus

SCENE 1: *Vineyard*

SCENE 2: *Man's house (set to one side of scene 1 so that both are seen together)*

SCENE:1

Vineyard owner: Come on, you lot. My new vineyard's nearly ready. The vines are planted, the walls are built, you've dug the pit for the winepress, and we've nearly finished the watchtower. Come on, let's get this final wall finished, then we can hand it over to the new tenants. *(All finish building the wall).* I'm going away now, but I hope you'll all work as well for the new master as you have done for me. I think he'll be a very fair master and that you'll all enjoy this new vineyard which you've all helped me to build. I'll take a few of you with me, then you can come back and collect the rent at harvest time. Now which of you wants to come with me, and which of you wants to stay?

1st builder: Master, you've been so good to us that we don't want to work for anyone else. Can't we all go with you?

Vineyard owner: No, I'm sorry, but I've just said that I'm only taking a few of you. The rest of you will have to stay here and work for the new tenant.

2nd builder: But we don't want to work for a stranger, we want to work for you. The new man might not be as good as you've been and so we might have to go on strike.

Vineyard owner: I'm sorry you feel like that, but I just can't afford to take you all with me. If you can't come to some agreement as to who'll come with me and who'll stay behind and work for the new tenant, then I'll just have to choose those I want to come with me.

(Master chooses three men and leaves)

2nd builder: Huh, just look at that. He's taken his favourites as usual. We might have known we didn't have a choice. Hmm. *(NEW TENANT enters).* Now who's this coming?

New tenant: Now what's going off here? Why is everybody looking so miserable?

1st builder: We might well look glum. We've just finished building this vineyard for our master, and he's just gone off with his favourites and left us all behind to work for you. That's gratitude for you. He says he'll send his servants back to collect the rent at harvest time. Who'll have done all the work by then, I ask you?

New tenant: Never mind. We'll make this vineyard into the best in the country. And as to his servants collecting the rent at harvest time, we'll see about that. *(Looking round at the disgruntled workers).* I think we're all going to get along fine.

SCENE: 2

Vineyard owner: Well, now it's harvest time. *(Turning to first servant).* Will you go back to our new vineyard and collect the rents, please, and bring some of the fruit back with you? It's been a good year for grapes, so there should be a good harvest.

(FIRST SERVANT leaves the VINEYARD OWNER, and enters the vineyard)

1st builder:	Hey, look who's here. The little favourite himself! Now what have you come back for?
First servant:	The master's sent me for the rent and for some fruit from his vineyard.
2nd builder:	Oh has he really? His vineyard indeed. I'd like to know who's put all the work into **his** vineyard. Who do you think you are, coming here and asking for money and fruit? We'll show you what we think about you and your master.

(FIRST SERVANT is seized, beaten and sent away empty handed. He returns to the VINEYARD OWNER).

Vineyard owner:	What did you say they did to you? As if I need ask. Just look at the state of you! I'll show them what's what. *(Turns to SECOND SERVANT).* You go, this time. They won't dare to treat another servant the same way.

(SECOND SERVANT leaves and goes to the vineyard)

1st builder:	Hey, look, folks. Here comes another of the favourites. Let's show him what's what, before he has chance to tell us what he wants.

(SECOND SERVANT is struck on the head and knocked about. He leaves and returns to his master)

Vineyard owner:	Not you as well! This will not do. *(Turns to THIRD SERVANT who starts to shake in fear).* You can go this time, and see if you can make them see sense.

(THIRD SERVANT leaves and enters vineyard)

2nd builder:	Hello, here comes another one. It doesn't seem as if our old master can take "No", for an answer. We'll show him this time, though.

(They take hold of the THIRD SERVANT and kill him).

Vineyard owner: Oh what more can I do? I've lost all my servants to these people and they still won't listen and do what I say. I've only one son, and he's all I have left, but I'll have to send him to reason with them. I know that they'll respect my son. They won't dare to touch him.

(SON leaves and enters vineyard)

1st builder: Oh, ho. Now look who's coming. He's sent his only son. This is the heir. Come on, let's kill him and the vineyard'll be ours.

(They take hold of the SON, kill him and throw him out of the vineyard)

Jesus: *(enters the scene)*
What do you think the owner of the vineyard will do now? He'll come and kill those tenants and give the vineyard to others who will give him his share of the crop. Haven't you read this scripture, "The stone the builders rejected has become the capstone; the Lord has done this and it is marvellous in our eyes?" Everyone who falls on that stone will be broken to pieces, but he on whom it falls will be crushed.

THE END

THE GREAT DIVIDE

Luke 16 : 19 - 31

Cast:

Rich man   Lazarus
Servant   Abraham

SCENE 1: *Rich man's dining room*

SCENE 2: *Rich man's gate*

SCENE 3: *Heaven and hell*

SCENE: 1

Rich man: *(dressed in purple)*
            Is there any more of that gorgeous gateau left? I don't really
            think I ought to eat any, but it's so yummy that I can't resist
            it.

Servant: Yes, master. *(Gives RICH MAN some more food)*

Rich man: That was good. I don't think my doctor knows what he's
            talking about, telling me that I eat too much. He says if I don't
            cut down then I'll die. What does he know? He's only jealous.

Servant: Yes, master.

Rich man: Well, I think I've had just about enough for the moment. Roll
            on supper time. You can clear away now. Give the dogs the
            scraps. Ha ha ha. We don't have very fat dogs round here, do
            we?

Servant: *(Clearing the table)*
            No master.

Rich man: I'm glad that you're a good, polite servant. Not like that last
            one I had, Lazarus, or whatever his name was. Very insolent
            chap, that. He had to go. *(SERVANT exits)* I wonder what
            happened to Lazarus? It must be a couple of months since I

threw him out into the street. *(Clutches his chest)* Oh, I do have a funny pain in my chest. Now it's going down my arm. I wonder ..... Get the doct......... Aaaaah! *(Falls to the floor dead).*

SCENE: 2

Lazarus: I don't know how much longer I can last, trying to live off the scraps he throws to the dogs. I'm starving!

Servant: You'll not get much from these scraps, I can tell you, Lazarus. I can't give you anything to eat either, as he always checks the kitchen cupboards at the end of every day, and he knows if there's anything missing or not. It would be more than my job's worth to try to feed you. It's a pity you didn't keep your mouth shut when you had a good job inside. Trust you to tell him what you thought about his being greedy. You've only yourself to blame for the state you're in. Just look at all those sores you've got. Even the dogs won't lick them for you much longer.

Lazarus: I won't be here much longer. I'm so weak that I don't think I'll last the night.

SCENE: 3

(LAZARUS is sitting at ABRAHAM'S side in Heaven and the RICH MAN is in hell. There is a great gulf in between Heaven and hell).

Rich man: Ooh, Father Abraham, have pity on me. It's so hot in here and I'm gagged. Send Lazarus to get me a little drink of water, will you, because I'm in agony in this fire?

Abraham: Son, remember when you were alive. You had all your good things then, and Lazarus only had bad things. Now he's comfortable here with me in heaven and you're in agony in hell. Anyway, there's a great big valley between you and us and it's impossible for anybody to cross it either way.

Rich man: In that case, Abraham, send Lazarus to my old house where my five brothers are living. Send him to warn them all so they won't have to come here as well.

Abraham: They have Moses and the prophets to listen to, just like you did. Let them listen to them.

Rich man: Father Abraham, they're not going to do that, but if somebody came back to visit them from the dead, then they would listen and they'd be sorry and they'd be good.

Abraham: If they won't listen to Moses and the prophets then they won't be convinced even if someone did come back and visit them even from the dead.

THE END

MOORLEY'S

are growing Publishers, adding several new titles to our list each year. We also undertake private publications and commissioned works.

Our range of publications
includes: **Books of Verse**
        Devotional Poetry
        Recitations
        Drama
        Bible Plays
        Sketches
        Nativity Plays
        Passiontide Plays
        Easter Plays
        Demonstrations
        Resource Books
        Assembly Material
        Songs & Musicals
        Children's Addresses
        Prayers & Graces
        Daily Readings
        Books for Speakers
        Activity Books
        Quizzes
        Puzzles
        Painting Books
        Daily Readings
        Church Stationery
        Notice Books
        Cradle Rolls
        Hymn Board Numbers

Please send a S.A.E. (approx 9" x 6") for the current catalogue or consult your local Christian Bookshop who should stock or be able to order our titles.